grade

6

D0475030

For full details of exam requirements, please refer to the current syllabus in conjunction with *Examination Information & Regulations* and the guide for candidates, teachers and parents, *These Music Exams*. These three documents are available online at www.abrsm.org, as well as free of charge from music retailers, from ABRSM local representatives or from the Services Department, The Associated Board of the Royal Schools of Music, 24 Portland Place, London W1B 1LU, United Kingdom.

REQUIREMENTS

SCALES AND ARPEGGIOS (from memory)

in Db, F, F# majors; C#, F, F# minors (two octaves)
A, Bb majors; A, Bb minors (three octaves)

Scales

in the above keys (minors in both melodic *and* harmonic forms):
(i)   separate bows, even notes
(ii)   slurred, seven notes to a bow

Chromatic Scales

starting on Ab, B and C (two octaves):
(i)   separate bows, even notes
(ii)   slurred, four *or* six notes to a bow at candidate's choice

Arpeggios

the common chords of the above keys:
(i)   separate bows, even notes
(ii)   slurred, six notes to a bow (two-octave arpeggios) and three notes to a bow (three-octave arpeggios)

Dominant Sevenths

in the keys of C, D and Eb (starting on G, A and Bb and resolving on the tonic) (two octaves):
(i)   separate bows, even notes
(ii)   slurred, four notes to a bow

Diminished Sevenths

starting on G and A (two octaves):
(i)   separate bows, even notes
(ii)   slurred, four notes to a bow

Double-Stop Scale

in sixths in Bb major (one octave): rhythm and bowing in broken steps

PLAYING AT SIGHT (see current syllabus)

AURAL TESTS (see current syllabus)

THREE PIECES

page

Candidates must prepare three pieces, one from each of the three Lists, A, B and C. Candidates may choose from the pieces printed in this album or any other piece listed for the grade. A full list is given in the current syllabus.

Violin consultant:
Edward Huws Jones
Footnotes: Clive Brown (CB),
Edward Huws Jones (EHJ), Richard
Jones (RJ) and Anthony Burton

DO NOT PHOTOCOPY
© MUSIC

Where appropriate, pieces in this album have been checked with original source material and edited as necessary for instructional purposes. Any editorial additions to the texts are given in small print, within square brackets, or – in the case of slurs and ties – in the form ⌐. Fingering, bowing, metronome marks and the editorial realization of ornaments are for guidance only; they are not comprehensive or obligatory.

Allegro con vivacità

First movement from Guitar Quintet No. 6 in G, G. 450

Arranged by
Edward Huws Jones

BOCCHERINI

Italian by birth, Luigi Boccherini (1743–1805) was much travelled, working for many years at the court of Spain – which explains his interest in chamber music featuring Spanish guitar. As well as being an astonishingly prolific composer, Boccherini was a cellist; this is reflected in his bass lines, which often sparkle with rhythmic interest and occasional melodic quirks. In this arrangement of a movement from his Guitar Quintet No. 6 the violin solo is close to Boccherini's original first violin line, while much of the guitar part is incorporated into the right hand of the piano.
EHJ

A:2

Allegro

Fourth movement from Sonata in D, HWV 371, Op. 1 No. 13

Edited and continuo realization by
Richard Jones

HANDEL

The Sonata in D, HWV 371, of which this Allegro forms the finale, is widely regarded as one of the finest of Handel's instrumental sonatas. It is a late work, dating from around 1750, when the composer was about 65 years old. Shortly after the sonata's composition, an abridged version of the finale was recycled as the music for the entrance of the angel in Handel's last oratorio, *Jephtha*. RJ
Source: autograph manuscript, London, British Library, R.M. 20.g.13

A:3

Vivace

First movement from Sonatina No. 6 in F, TWV 41:F1

Edited and continuo realization by
Richard Jones

TELEMANN

Georg Philipp Telemann (1681–1767), one of the most prolific composers of his day, became city music director at Frankfurt and Kapellmeister at the Barfüsserkirche in 1712. He gave regular weekly concerts with the local Collegium musicum, performing his own vocal and instrumental works. In 1715 he began to publish his own music, and his earliest published collections of instrumental music include the six sonatinas for violin and harpsichord of 1718, from which this Vivace is drawn. The first-time bar at the end of the second strain (b. 30a) is editorial. In the exam, both repeats should be played. Players might like to vary the dynamics on the second playing, and perhaps introduce some simple embellishment. RJ

Source: *Sei sonatine per violino e cembalo* (Amsterdam: le Cene, 1724/5)

Non giova il sospirar

B:1

Arranged by
Charles-Auguste de Bériot

Edited by
Sheila Nelson

DONIZETTI

Like most Italian composers of the 19th century, Gaetano Donizetti (1797–1848) worked chiefly in the opera house; but he also wrote many instrumental pieces, cantatas, sacred works and songs. His 'Venetian canzonetta' *Non giova il sospirar* (Sighing is of no use), subtitled 'Jealousy', was one of a group of three songs for voice and piano which he published in 1822. This transcription for violin and piano is from a set of *12 Italian Songs* by Charles-Auguste de Bériot (1802–70), the Belgian violinist and composer who was one of the pioneers of the Romantic style of violin playing.

B:2

Chanson de nuit

Op. 15 No. 1

Edited by
Clive Brown

ELGAR

Edward Elgar (1857–1934) earned his living mainly as a violin teacher and professional violinist until he was over 40 years old. As well as his magnificent Violin Concerto and Sonata, his output includes more than twenty smaller pieces for violin and piano, written mostly while he was struggling to gain recognition as a composer. In *Chanson de nuit* (Night Song), published in 1897, Elgar provided his own fingerings, which are often designed to achieve the tone colour of a particular string or facilitate the expressive portamento that was characteristic of his own playing. Some easier alternatives have been suggested, in editorial brackets, but players would benefit from considering Elgar's fingerings. CB

Fine

Tempo di minuetto

in the style of Gaetano Pugnani

KREISLER

B:3

Fritz Kreisler (1875–1962), Austrian-born though later an American citizen, was the supreme violin virtuoso of his time. As a composer, he had a gift for writing short pieces in styles of the past, which he frequently included in his recitals. But, feeling it would be 'impudent and tactless' to give his own name too much exposure, he passed them off as editions of pieces by minor and conveniently obscure figures. This Minuet, like his well-known *Praeludium and Allegro*, he attributed to the Turin violinist and composer Gaetano Pugnani (1731–98). The marking *Martiale* (*marziale*, or 'martial') is unexpected in a dance piece: perhaps we should imagine a minuet danced by a soldier!

AB 3281

C:1

Tico-Tico Bird in the Cornmeal

Arranged by
Edward Huws Jones

ABREU

Tico-tico no fubá – to give this piece its Portuguese title – was composed by Zequinha de Abreu (1880–1935) and has become one of the best-known Brazilian tunes. It first became popular in the USA during the 1940s and was recorded by numerous artists, from Charlie Parker and Henry Mancini to Donald Duck (in the Disney film *Saludos Amigos*). There are vocal versions, which are often performed a little slower, but as an instrumental piece it needs to be played fast and accurately. Play the quavers with short strokes around the middle of the bow; the crotchets and tied notes should be detached for rhythmic precision and to create the accents. EHJ

Fine

Nocturne

C:2

Edited by
Richard Jones

L. BOULANGER

Lili Boulanger (1893–1918) was a French composer and younger sister of the famous composition teacher Nadia Boulanger. In 1913 she became the first woman to win the coveted composition prize the Prix de Rome. An invalid from childhood, her brilliant career as a composer was tragically cut short when she died at the age of only 24. RJ

Source: *Nocturne* (Paris: Ricordi, 1918)

C:3

Youngsters' Dance

No. 19 from *24 Easy Little Concert Pieces*

SZELÉNYI

The Hungarian composer István Szelényi (1904–72) was a pupil of Zoltán Kodály and an advocate of his educational methods; he taught for many years at the Budapest Conservatory and the Budapest Academy of Music. His compositions include orchestral, choral and chamber works, and many teaching pieces. The main tune of this *Youngsters' Dance*, from a collection published in 1958, is in an unusual metre of 11 quavers to the bar, most commonly found in Bulgarian folk music; other passages are in a freer mixture of time signatures.

AB 3281

poco a poco cresc.

poco a poco cresc.

grade 6

For full details of exam requirements, please refer to the current syllabus in conjunction with *Examination Information & Regulations* and the guide for candidates, teachers and parents, *These Music Exams*. These three documents are available online at www.abrsm.org, as well as free of charge from music retailers, from ABRSM local representatives or from the Services Department, The Associated Board of the Royal Schools of Music, 24 Portland Place, London W1B 1LU, United Kingdom.

Violin & Piano
Piano only

CONTENTS AND TRACK LISTING

Where appropriate, pieces in this album have been checked with original source material and edited as necessary for instructional purposes. Any editorial additions to the texts are given in small print, within square brackets, or – in the case of slurs and ties – in the form ⌒. Fingering, bowing, metronome marks and the editorial realization of ornaments are for guidance only; they are not comprehensive or obligatory.

Violin consultant: Edward Huws Jones
Footnotes: Clive Brown (CB), Edward Huws Jones (EHJ), Richard Jones (RJ) and Anthony Burton

Alternative pieces for this grade

Music origination by Barnes Music Engraving Ltd
Cover by Økvik Design
Printed in England by Caligraving Ltd, Thetford, Norfolk

Allegro con vivacità

First movement from Guitar Quintet No. 6 in G, G. 450

Arranged by
Edward Huws Jones

BOCCHERINI

Italian by birth, Luigi Boccherini (1743–1805) was much travelled, working for many years at the court of Spain – which explains his interest in chamber music featuring Spanish guitar. As well as being an astonishingly prolific composer, Boccherini was a cellist; this is reflected in his bass lines, which often sparkle with rhythmic interest and occasional melodic quirks. In this arrangement of a movement from his Guitar Quintet No. 6 the violin solo is close to Boccherini's original first violin line, while much of the guitar part is incorporated into the right hand of the piano.
EHJ

AB 3281

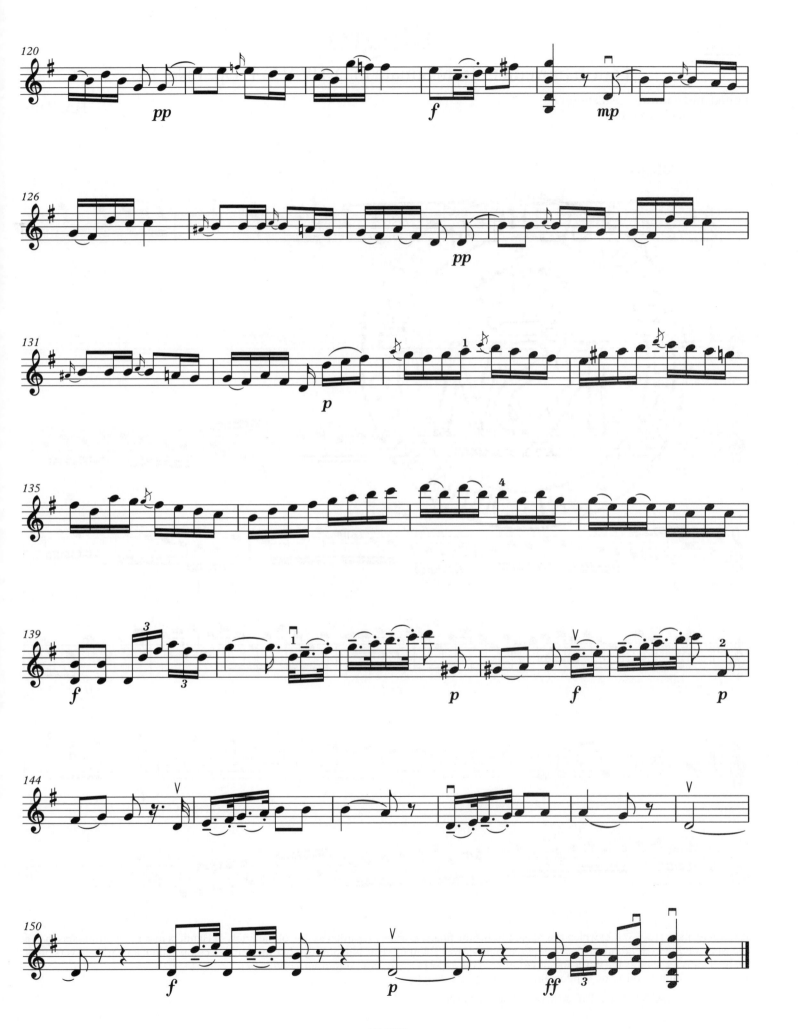

A:2

Allegro

Fourth movement from Sonata in D, HWV 371, Op. 1 No. 13

Edited and continuo realization by
Richard Jones

HANDEL

The Sonata in D, HWV 371, of which this Allegro forms the finale, is widely regarded as one of the finest of Handel's instrumental sonatas. It is a late work, dating from around 1750, when the composer was about 65 years old. Shortly after the sonata's composition, an abridged version of the finale was recycled as the music for the entrance of the angel in Handel's last oratorio, *Jephtha*. RJ
Source: autograph manuscript, London, British Library, R.M. 20.g.13

A:3

Vivace

First movement from Sonatina No. 6 in F, TWV 41:F1

Edited and continuo realization by
  Richard Jones

TELEMANN

Georg Philipp Telemann (1681–1767), one of the most prolific composers of his day, became city music director at Frankfurt and Kapellmeister at the Barfüsserkirche in 1712. He gave regular weekly concerts with the local Collegium musicum, performing his own vocal and instrumental works. In 1715 he began to publish his own music, and his earliest published collections of instrumental music include the six sonatinas for violin and harpsichord of 1718, from which this Vivace is drawn. In the exam, both repeats should be played. Players might like to vary the dynamics on the second playing, and perhaps introduce some simple embellishment. RJ

Source: *Sei sonatine per violino e cembalo* (Amsterdam: le Cene, 1724/5)

B:1

Non giova il sospirar

Arranged by
Charles-Auguste de Bériot

Edited by
Sheila Nelson

DONIZETTI

Like most Italian composers of the 19th century, Gaetano Donizetti (1797–1848) worked chiefly in the opera house; but he also wrote many instrumental pieces, cantatas, sacred works and songs. His 'Venetian canzonetta' *Non giova il sospirar* (Sighing is of no use), subtitled 'Jealousy', was one of a group of three songs for voice and piano which he published in 1822. This transcription for violin and piano is from a set of *12 Italian Songs* by Charles-Auguste de Bériot (1802–70), the Belgian violinist and composer who was one of the pioneers of the Romantic style of violin playing.

B:2

Chanson de nuit

Op. 15 No. 1

Edited by
Clive Brown

ELGAR

Edward Elgar (1857–1934) earned his living mainly as a violin teacher and professional violinist until he was over 40 years old. As well as his magnificent Violin Concerto and Sonata, his output includes more than twenty smaller pieces for violin and piano, written mostly while he was struggling to gain recognition as a composer. In *Chanson de nuit* (Night Song), published in 1897, Elgar provided his own fingerings, which are often designed to achieve the tone colour of a particular string or facilitate the expressive portamento that was characteristic of his own playing. Some easier alternatives have been suggested, in editorial brackets, but players would benefit from considering Elgar's fingerings. CB

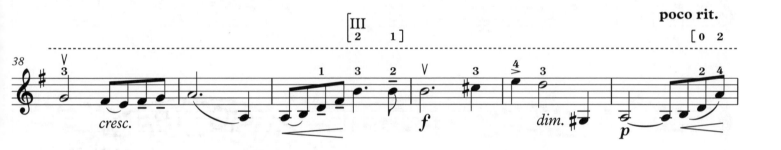

b. 49: the wedge-shaped articulation mark above the final quaver is puzzling. However, it is present in both the score and separate violin part in the first edition and so was presumably intended by the composer. In view of the two fermatas and the already peculiarly precise length of the note, it is hard to see what musical meaning it could have been intended to convey. Perhaps this is a little Elgarian joke. CB

B:3

Tempo di minuetto

in the style of Gaetano Pugnani

KREISLER

Fritz Kreisler (1875–1962), Austrian-born though later an American citizen, was the supreme violin virtuoso of his time. As a composer, he had a gift for writing short pieces in styles of the past, which he frequently included in his recitals. But, feeling it would be 'impudent and tactless' to give his own name too much exposure, he passed them off as editions of pieces by minor and conveniently obscure figures. This Minuet, like his well-known *Praeludium and Allegro*, he attributed to the Turin violinist and composer Gaetano Pugnani (1731–98). The marking *Martiale* (*marziale*, or 'martial') is unexpected in a dance piece: perhaps we should imagine a minuet danced by a soldier!

C:1

Tico-Tico Bird in the Cornmeal

Arranged by
Edward Huws Jones

ABREU

Tico-tico no fubá – to give this piece its Portuguese title – was composed by Zequinha de Abreu (1880–1935) and has become one of the best-known Brazilian tunes. It first became popular in the USA during the 1940s and was recorded by numerous artists, from Charlie Parker and Henry Mancini to Donald Duck (in the Disney film *Saludos Amigos*). There are vocal versions, which are often performed a little slower, but as an instrumental piece it needs to be played fast and accurately. Play the quavers with short strokes around the middle of the bow; the crotchets and tied notes should be detached for rhythmic precision and to create the accents. EHJ

D.S. al Fine

Nocturne

C:2

Edited by
Richard Jones

L. BOULANGER

Lili Boulanger (1893–1918) was a French composer and younger sister of the famous composition teacher Nadia Boulanger. In 1913 she became the first woman to win the coveted composition prize the Prix de Rome. An invalid from childhood, her brilliant career as a composer was tragically cut short when she died at the age of only 24. RJ
Source: *Nocturne* (Paris: Ricordi, 1918)

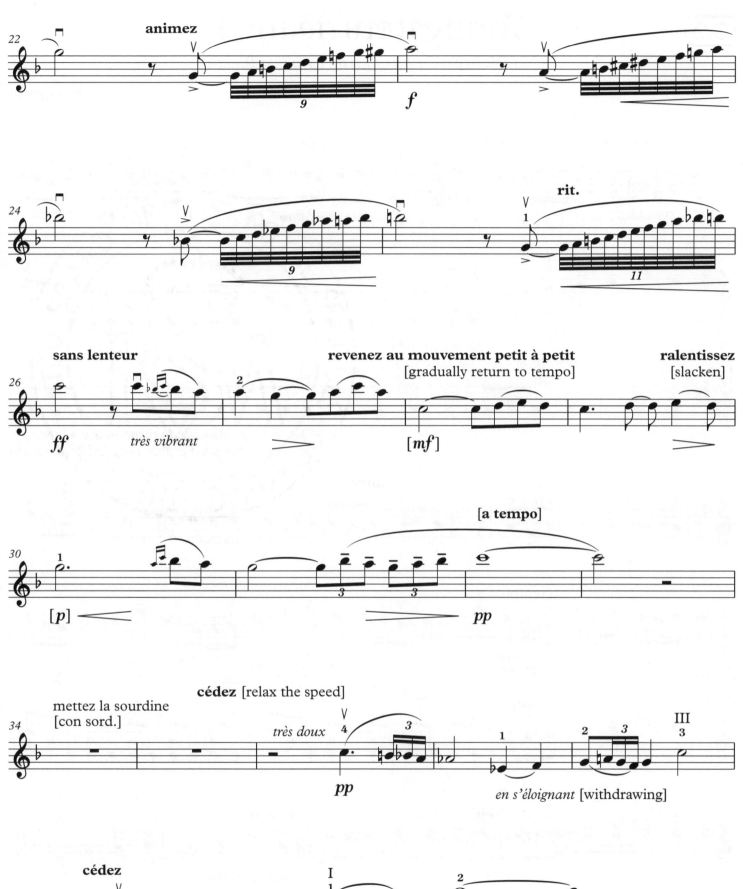

C:3

Youngsters' Dance

No. 19 from *24 Easy Little Concert Pieces*

SZELÉNYI

The Hungarian composer István Szelényi (1904–72) was a pupil of Zoltán Kodály and an advocate of his educational methods; he taught for many years at the Budapest Conservatory and the Budapest Academy of Music. His compositions include orchestral, choral and chamber works, and many teaching pieces. The main tune of this *Youngsters' Dance*, from a collection published in 1958, is in an unusual metre of 11 quavers to the bar, most commonly found in Bulgarian folk music; other passages are in a freer mixture of time signatures.

poco a poco cresc.

ff

senza dim. sin' al fine

sff